WEATHER

(Original French title: *La météo*)

by
Pierre Kohler

Translated from the French by
Albert V. Carozzi and Marguerite Carozzi

First English language edition published in 1988 by Barron's Educational Series, Inc.

© 1985 Hachette S.A., 79, boulevard Saint-Germain, 75006 Paris

The title of the French edition is *La météo*.

Library of Congress Catalog Card

International Standard Book No. 0

G000278687

New York • London • Toronto • Sydney

PRINTED IN FRANCE

789 9687 987654321

Contents

Astronauts who landed on the Moon did not have to worry about meteorology! If you look at pictures taken at the surface of our satellite, you will notice that the sky is always black.

Why does lunar meteorology not exist? Simply because the Moon has no atmosphere. All the vagaries of weather we experience are caused by the layer of air that surrounds us, called atmosphere. More precisely, the realm of weather is limited to a thin layer, about 12 kilometers (7.5 miles) thick, called troposphere. This is the "meteorological" atmosphere.

Pushed by the winds of the monsoon, *clouds are building up above the plain of the Ganges River. Soon the long-awaited rain will fall, but there also will be floods.*

What Makes the Weather?

In the troposphere, the atmosphere is far from quiet. Everywhere, air keeps moving, now in this direction, now in another. In certain places, water vapor suddenly condenses to form clouds; these clouds may be very high in the sky such as cirrus, or rapidly expanding and puffy such as cumulus, or, on the con-

Weather represents a battle between masses of cold air and warm air. Sometimes cold air lifts warm air, but at other times warm air glides over cold air. The boundary surface between contrasting air masses is called a front. When this front moves, the weather changes.

trary, close to the ground, causing fog. Clouds often condense to form rain, and under certain conditions of temperature, raindrops are transformed into snowflakes. Winds may blow with ex-

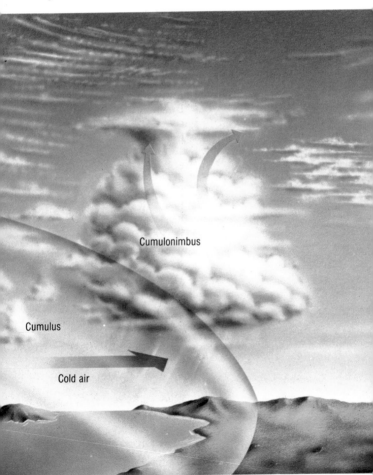

Cumulonimbus

Cumulus

Cold air

treme violence and cause storms or even hurricanes.

A mixture of all these processes is what we call weather. We all know how our activities are related to weather conditions.

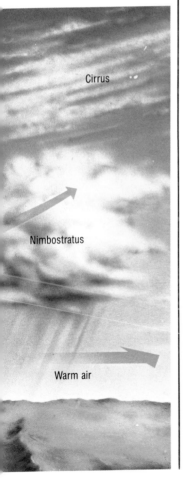

Cirrus

Nimbostratus

Warm air

The Battle Between Air Masses

Before reviewing the different effects of weather, let us quickly see how the great meteorological machine of the Earth works.

To start with, there are large air masses. If the ground surface of our planet had the same temperature everywhere, air would be perfectly homogeneous. But this is obviously not the case. The first reason is that the Earth does not receive solar rays evenly. It is warmer at the equator, where rays arrive almost vertically, than at the poles, where they hit the surface almost horizontally or not at all in winter. Second, seasons must be taken into account. According to the time of year, the Earth is more or less inclined on its axis with respect to the Sun so that solar rays hit the surface at an angle that changes continuously. You know that the Sun is higher in the sky in summer than in winter.

Hot air rises just as a bubble floats up from the bottom of a container to the surface. Above the equator, where it is very hot, air thus rises while flowing either northward or southward. Inversely, in polar regions, where it is much colder, air moves toward the equator to fill, so to speak, the "void" left by the risen warm air. In contact with the ground and the ocean surfaces, cold air will soon become warm and rise in turn, and the equatorial air will descend after having cooled off. The cycle is thus completed.

At least, this is what would happen if the Earth did not move. However, our planet rotates on its axis and this movement results, in the northern hemisphere, in an eastward deflection—in the direction of the rotation—of the large air cells thus formed. This is called the Coriolis force. In other words, this force causes all winds in the northern hemisphere to move to the right and those in the southern hemisphere to move to the left.

Moreover, the surface of

Man on the Moon in broad daylight. *The Sun shines but the sky is black. This is so because the Moon has no atmosphere, nothing that solar rays could color.*

Pictures of the Earth taken by satellites *allow scientists to observe the distribution of air masses and to predict their evolution.*

the Earth is not the same everywhere. On the one hand, there are vast ocean surfaces, and on the other hand, continents, which are very variable themselves, having features such as deserts, prairies, forests, ice covers, or interior seas. These surfaces absorb and reflect solar radiation in various ways that locally disturb the movement of the atmosphere.

A Regular Cycle: The Monsoon

At the surface of the Earth exist a certain number of regular winds that were well-known and appreciated by navigators at the time of sailing ships. Such is the case in particular of the trade winds that blow from the northeast, between the subtropical high-pressure belt and the equa-

Meteorological Phenomena

Certain atmospheric phenomena are strange or spectacular. The ancient Greeks called these meteors *(things in the air). Today a meteor means any atmospheric phenomenon, like hail, or typhoons. Some belong to the realm of light, others to that of precipitations.*

One of the best-known light phenomena is the rainbow, which appears when it rains while solar rays filter between two clouds. This large colored semicircle is visible only when the observer turns his back to the Sun. From the interior toward the exterior of the rainbow, one sees the colors of the spectrum in the following order: violet, blue, green, yellow, orange, and red. Sometimes a second rainbow can be seen, which is larger, and less luminous, and has its colors reversed. A rainbow is caused by refraction of solar rays through large drops of water as through a prism. There is no rainbow if drops are smaller than 1/10 millimeter in diameter. Such a phenomenon of light refraction also causes halos around the Moon or the Sun when clouds formed by ice crystals (cirrostratus) are located directly in front of these heavenly bodies. An example of a spectacular meteorological phenomenon is hail; a less spectacular but much more common one is rain.

tor. But the same sailors were afraid of storms that started regularly in the southern hemisphere between 40° and 50° latitude, hence the name "the roaring forties" given to that area.

People living on land are also concerned about certain regular winds that may be both beneficial and deadly. The best known are the monsoons of India and Southeast Asia, which strongly influence the life of the inhabitants.

During summer, the Asian continent heats up and atmospheric pressure drops. A high-pressure system in the Indian Ocean causes winds to blow from the ocean to the land—that is, from the southwest or from the area of the Seychelles (a group of islands in the Indian Ocean). During its long travel above the warm tropical waters, the air increases in humidity and condenses into rainfall when it reaches the coasts of Asia. This rainfall is the summer monsoon, which normally begins in mid-June. Although it often causes floods, the summer monsoon is most welcome for crops. However, sometimes for two years in a row (for instance, as in 1973 and 1974), the monsoons do not bring substantial rain, and droughts and famine occur.

In winter, the monsoon circulation is reversed. Air flows from the Himalaya toward the ocean: this is the dry winter monsoon, which blows from the northeast.

On a smaller scale, land and sea breezes that blow in

In Southeast Asia, torrential monsoon rains are beneficial for agriculture. However, every year, they claim many lives and are responsible for important material damage.

the morning and in the evening along coastal areas demonstrate the same phenomenon of temperature differences between land and sea.

Anticyclones and Low Pressure Systems: Sibling Rivalries

The atmosphere is divided into many high-pressure and low-pressure systems. In general, atmospheric pressure is low where the climate is hot, and high where it is cold. High-pressure systems are called anticyclones; areas of low atmospheric pressure are called depressions, or cyclones. These are most often referred to simply as highs and lows. They represent the relief of the atmosphere that is naturally invisible. Just as rivers flow down from a mountain into a valley, winds flow from high- to low-pressure areas. The greater the difference in pressure, the stronger the winds.

Air masses carry clouds that represent cooled water vapor, called moisture. Any volume of air contains invisible moisture. However, for a given volume, cold air contains less moisture than warm air. Therefore, a mass of cold air that is forced to rise condenses and eventually releases excess moisture, forming a cloud. As long as the ascending currents coming from the ground are sufficiently strong, the cloud remains in this state and moves with the winds. Otherwise, water in the cloud starts falling: it rains.

Wind and rain are two weather processes. Also, according to particular conditions at a given time, we may have either snow, fog, frost, hail, or storms. All these processes represent weather.

On the right are six varieties of clouds with their characteristic appearance.
1. **Cirrus:** *cloud with a fibrous look; it is composed of very scattered ice crystals.*
2. **Cumulus humilis:** *cloud that forecasts fair weather; also called fair-weather cumulus.*
3. **Cumulus congestus:** *cloud endowed with powerful vertical updrafts; such a cloud may bring showers.*
4. **Contrails:** *clouds produced artificially by exhaust fumes of jet planes flying at high altitude.*
5. **Cumulonimbus:** *clouds that forecast rainstorms, hail or high winds.*
6. **Tornado:** *whirlpool of rapidly moving air with a funnel shape, which develops under a cumulonimbus when a cold front comes in contact with an overheated ground surface.*

11

Weather Forecasting

Men have long been interested in weather forecasting. As long ago as about 350 B.C., Artistotle wrote Meteorologica (a treatise on meteorology). But it was not until the sixteenth century that instruments were invented to forecast weather, and not until the last century that the scientific methods that actually gave rise to modern meteorology were developed.

At the beginning of the seventeenth century, Leonardo da Vinci built a weather vane to find out where winds blew from. Today, weather vanes can be found almost everywhere—but in particular, on top of public buildings and church steeples.

Other meteorological instruments appeared in the next century, most of them in a time span of less than forty years, namely between 1640 and 1680. They are, in chronological order: the *hygrometer* (invented by Ferdinand II of Tuscany); the *anemometer* (by the English scholar Robert Hooke); the *thermometer* (by the Dutch physicist Christian Huygens, but already visualized by Galileo in 1593); the *barometer* (by the Italian physicist Torricelli); and the *pluviometer* or *rain gauge* (used for the first time by the English scientist Towneley).

If Your Hair Frizzes, the Air Is Humid

The hygrometer measures the percentage of humidity in the air. However, the first instruments were in reality only hygroscopes, which allowed one to know only whether the air was dry or humid, according to the behavior of a ball of wool.

The first measurement, based on the lengthening or the shortening of a human

This rudimentary weather station dates from the beginning of this century.
It was located on top of the Saint-Jacques Tower in Paris (France).

13

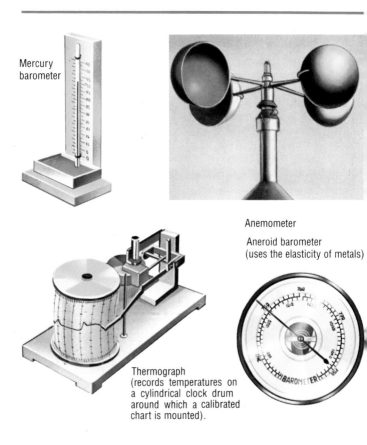

Mercury barometer

Anemometer

Aneroid barometer
(uses the elasticity of metals)

Thermograph
(records temperatures on
a cylindrical clock drum
around which a calibrated
chart is mounted).

hair, was done in 1783 by Horace-Bénédict de Saussure, who actually built a hygrometer. Human hair is indeed very sensitive to humidity. This is why many people have frizzy hair when it rains.

Speed Limit: 150 Kilometers Per Hour (93.7 Miles Per Hour)

The anemometer, which is often associated with a weather vane, measures wind speed. Three or four metal cups (which resemble small balls cut in half) are mounted on arms that rotate freely about a vertical axis. The instrument resembles a merry-go-round, which turns more or less fast depending on wind speed.

The speed can be measured by counting the number of rotations made by the anemometer in one minute. However, the instrument is generally hooked up to a recorder that provides direct reading of the speed. Above 150 kilometers per hour (93.7 miles per hour), it is difficult to measure wind speed with precision, because the force of the wind destroys most anemometers.

Fahrenheit, Celsius, and Kelvin

A thermometer measures the temperature of the air. A liquid that expands with heat (mercury, alcohol) is put into a small sealed glass container consisting of a bulb connected to a thin stem. When the temperature increases, the li-

A radiosonde (enlarged in the upper left-corner circle) about to be released will be carried aloft by a hydrogen-filled balloon.

quid expands out of the bulb and rises into the stem. Inversely, when the temperature drops, the liquid column goes down. All that needs to be done is to engrave a measuring scale on the side of the stem so that we can read the temperature.

The most often used scale worldwide is the Centigrade scale proposed by the Swedish astronomer Anders Celsius in 1736. Zero corresponds to the melting point of ice, and 100 to the boiling point of water. Earlier, in 1714, a German instrument maker, Gabriel

Forecasting Without Instruments

For many centuries, people working or living outdoors, such as farmers or sailors, made a number of correct observations on weather forecasting based merely on natural phenomena. They translated these observations into folk proverbs easy to memorize. You may recognize some, or perhaps your family has some other favorites.

— *Red sky at night, sailor's delight.*
  Red sky at morning, sailor's warning.
— *April showers bring May flowers.*
— *March comes in like a lion*
  And goes out like a lamb.
— *Rain, rain go away*
  Come again another day.
— *It's raining cats and dogs.*
— *Make hay while the sun shines.*

Launching of a sounding balloon. *Every day, some weather station launch sounding balloons which carry recording instruments to provide profile of the atmosphere at high altitude. Measurements taken at ground level are not sufficient for accurate weather forecasting.*

Daniel Fahrenheit, had invented a mercury-in-glass thermometer with a scale interval of 180 degrees between the freezing and boiling points of water. This thermometer is still in use in the United States and Canada.

The Centigrade and Fahrenheit scales have negative, that is, below zero temperatures. For physicists, the only valid scale is that invented by the British mathematician and physicist William Kelvin, where the absolute zero represents the lowest possible temperature found in the universe. It represents $-273°C$ but has never been obtained in the laboratory.

Ten Meters (32 Feet) of Water to Forecast Weather

A barometer measures atmospheric pressure, that is, the weight of air. The first barometer was invented about

Weather stations (top). In the foreground: instruments to record temperature and humidity. In the middle ground: three rain gauges. In the background: telemeter to measure the elevation of clouds.

"France II" (bottom). A stationary weather ship.

the same time as the thermometer. It was a transparent tube filled with water that was plunged into a container also filled with water. Air pressure, exerting a different weight from one day to the next on the surface of the container, made water rise or fall accordingly in the tube; however, since water is not a dense liquid, a 10 meter-high (32 foot) water column was necessary to balance the weight of the air column!

In 1641, Giovanni Baliani built such an instrument along the wall of his house so that the transparent column was exactly in front of his bedroom window. On the surface of the water column floated a cork statuette. If he could see the statuette when he awoke, the weather was going to be fine; otherwise, he knew that the barometer level was too low and that it was going to rain! Two years later, his fellow countryman Torricelli had the idea to replace water by a denser liquid: mercury. A column of lesser height—on the average, 76 centimeters (29.92 inches)—was then sufficient to balance air pressure. Torricelli thus invented the mercury barometer. However, this instrument, although very precise, is so fragile and cumbersome that aneroid barometers are frequently used instead. These consist of a small metal capsule in which a vacuum has been established. The capsule tends to collapse when air pressure increases and to expand when pressure decreases, thus activating a needle that moves along a calibrated dial. Barometers found in many households are of this type.

The Simplest of Meteorological Instruments: The Rain Gauge

Precipitation is measured by the rain gauge (pluviometer). It is a simple container placed about 1 meter (39

The Kerguelen Islands in the subantarctic zone of the Southern Ocean are *an ideal place for meteorologists (below). They provide weather data on atmospheric conditions in the southern hemisphere where weather stations are scarce.*

inches) above the ground to avoid spattering, which would distort measurements. It is calibrated and allows direct reading of the amount of rainfall.

In this century, more sophisticated instruments were invented, such as the radiosonde, a hydrogen-filled balloon, about 2 meters (78 inches) in diameter, which carries up to an altitude of 25 kilometers (15.6 miles) a lightweight box fitted with recording instruments (thermometer, barometer, hygrometer). Data are transmitted by radio to a ground station where they are translated into atmospheric profiles at various altitudes. These data improve weather forecasting. The radiosonde was invented in 1927 by the French meteorologists Bureau and Hydrac, but almost thirty years earlier, in 1898, sounding balloons without radio transmitters had been launched by Teisserenc de Bort.

Satellites and Computers: A new Dimension Added to Meteorology

A new dimension in the study of the atmosphere is provided by earth-orbiting satellites and by computers. These are not, properly speaking, meteorological instruments, but they contribute importantly to the field of forecasting. The first weather satellites (called "Tiros") were put into orbit in 1960. However, the quality of their pictures was mediocre, and they provided only partial views of the Earth.

Today, geostationary (or earth-synchronous) satellites orbit the Earth at a height of approximately 35,900 kilometers (22,300 miles). From this altitude they can detect half of our planet at any one time. Every hour they send us a color image that shows changes in cloud systems and that allows us to predict the path of tropical cyclones or other severe storm systems. They can also make measurements of temperatures so that climatic trends from year to year can be known. Everyday, televi-

Weather satellites, in contact with receiving stations on the ground, continuously provide maps of the atmosphere and of its movements viewed from space. These maps are sometimes seen on our television screens during weather reports.

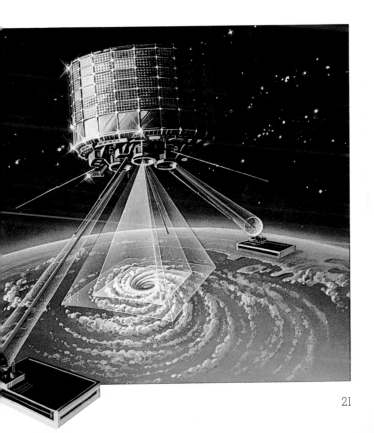

sion networks show satellite imagery of weather conditions. Five orbiting satellites are part of a global network.

Computers can provide detailed forecasts in a matter of seconds. Such calculations would never have been possible with pencil and paper. Thus, all these new techniques are providing more accurate research methods.

Storm in the Black Sea

It was in 1655 in Florence, Italy, that naturalists began to watch the sky on a regular basis and to make observations with the few meteorological instruments that existed then. These observations are extremely valuable today because they allow us to compare the weather of that time and the weather today. A major catastrophe occurred in 1854 that led weather forecasting to become more scientific. The French fleet was deployed in the Black Sea besieging Sevastopol (a seaport in Southern Ukraine, part of the Soviet Union today). The weather was calm when suddenly an extraordinarily severe storm hit the Black Sea and destroyed the fleet in a matter of hours. Napoleon III was furious and asked his minister of war Vaillant to start an inquiry in order to determine whether such a disastrous event could have been predicted. Le Verrier, director of the Paris Observatory, carried out the inquiry. In the course of his investigation, the French astronomer then discovered that most European universities were in the habit of recording weather conditions and that with this information it would have been possible to follow the movement of the disturbance across Europe to the Black Sea.

Le Verrier then proposed the creation of a European network of weather stations whose daily gathering of records would allow mete-

orologists to forecast the weather 48 hours in advance. Only three years after the disaster at Sevastopol, about ten stations had been created whose records were distributed in the form of a daily weather bulletin by a central station at the Paris Observatory. These bulletins were at first meant only for navigators, but soon forecasting became more general.

Stations by the Thousands

Today, almost every country on Earth has a weather service. More than 9,200 recording stations are distributed all over the globe to monitor atmospheric conditions every three hours. The geographical distribution of these stations shows, however, a great unevenness, since 80% of them are in the northern hemisphere. To these land-based stations can be added especially equipped weather ships, which are on constant duty in the Atlantic and Pacific Oceans; automatic weather buoys; and, above all, nearly 7,400 freighters that on a voluntary basis collect data used for weather predictions.

A global watch of the atmosphere uses polar-orbiting satellites and geostationary satellites stationed over the equator at various longitudes around the globe.

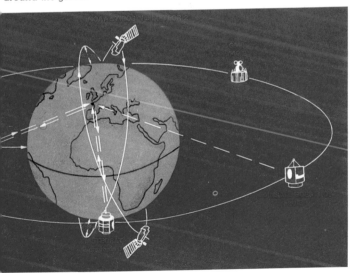

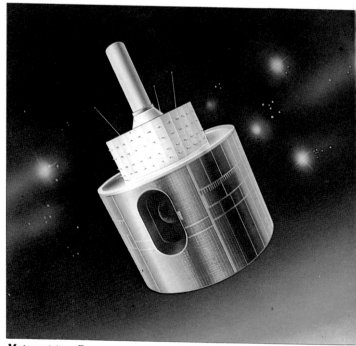

Meteosat *is a European weather satellite that since 1977 regularly produces a map of the upper atmosphere above the European continent. In the United States, the National Center for Atmospheric Research and the National Weather Service are responsible for the collection by satellites of weather data and their distribution.*

This global meteorological network is made more complete, as mentioned earlier, by about ten especially equipped satellites that take pictures of cloud systems from space. But how does one proceed from the data gathered from all these sources to weather prediction?

Before meteorology became a science with its recording instruments, its satellites, and its computers, weather forecasting was initially based on empirical observations that were transmitted from generation to generation. Some farmers continue to predict the weather on the basis of observations of natural events and the behavior of plants and animals. At present, however, weather forecasts are based strictly on rigorous scientific methods.

Forecasting: A Difficult Science

First of all, central stations in each state or country collect weather data that may be useful for their region. [In this book, we shall describe as an example the French weather system, because Le Verrier is considered the father of meteorology.] Coded data sent every three hours to central stations are the basis upon which detailed weather maps can then be established. These maps indicate weather conditions not only at ground level, but also at various altitudes, thus showing the atmosphere as a three-dimensional volume.

Electronic instruments of this ocean buoy allow scientists to study variation in ocean currents. Ocean buoys provide important weather information, relayed to an artificial satellite by radio, to navigators, fishermen, and yachtsmen.

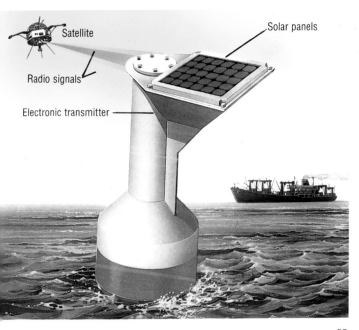

Satellite

Solar panels

Radio signals

Electronic transmitter

A rapid forecast is made for the general public by serial comparison of the maps. Thus, it is possible to predict the development of a disturbance and its course, or the increase of a high-pressure system that will result in a widespread fair-weather zone. From the general location of highs and lows, it is easy to deduce wind speed and direction. The evolution of large air masses also allows meteorologists to predict warming or cooling trends, the formation of fog, or the occurrence of thunder storms.

A more precise method consists of feeding into a computer all the atmospheric data (for instance, pressure, temperature, and humidity) for each box of a grid plotted for a certain region. The computer is programmed to take into account all these data and to forecast the weather for the next day, the day after next, three days later, and so forth. However, it has been observed that forecasts become increasingly less accurate with time.

Every square box of the grid is 250 kilometers (156

Is Meteorological War Possible?

After traditional, nuclear, and biological warfare, meteorological war has been mentioned more than once. Several science fiction novels were written on this topic. The International Research Institute for Peace (SIPRI) in Stockholm considers that a certain number of actions to change weather in order to harm an enemy are already possible. For instance, a nuclear explosion in the crater of a volcano would cause the expulsion of extraordinary quantities of matter into the atmosphere; a tsunami artificially produced by a powerful submarine explosion would set up conditions for a mini-hurricane.

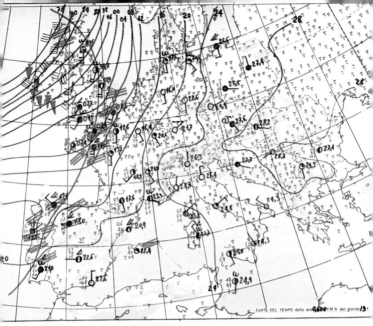

One of the many European weather maps, showing the symbols used by meteorologists.

25.4 atmospheric pressure
(25.4 = 1025.4 millibar; 89.6 = 989.6 millibar).

[For values of pressure close to 1000 millibar, the hundred and thousand numbers were omitted for reasons of simplification. Higher numbers starting with 9 (989.6 millibar) and smaller numbers starting with 10 (1016.4 millibar) are simply written as 89.6 and 16.4, respectively.]

———— Isobar

———— cold front

3   temperature

56   visibility

⌐   humidity

≡   winds measured at various altitudes

⅃   wind speed and direction

○   clear sky

◔   sky quarter-covered

◐   sky half-covered

◕   sky almost completely covered

●   sky completely covered

▼   storm clouds

ↄ   cirrus

▼   showers

≡   rainfall

═   fog

⫻   nimbostratus

∠   altostratus

ɯ   altocumulus

ℕ   stratocumulus

- - -   stratus

27

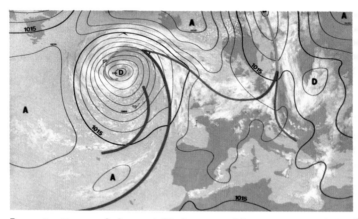

Reconstruction, made from satellite imagery, *of the organization of cloud systems in relationship to atmospheric circulation. A: High   D: Low*

miles) wide. In order to forecast the weather for the next 24 hours, the computer has to complete 15 billion calculations, which it can do in half an hour. For a five-day weather forecast, 10 hours of computer time are needed. Moreover, to improve the forecast by plotting boxes two times smaller, the computer time would have to be 20 times longer. More powerful computers would therefore be required to make this forecast within a reasonable time.

The largest high-speed computers in the world are in the Cray series and are used for weather forecasting. In order to predict weather a week in advance, they make one thousand billion calculations, which take seven computer-hours. This shows how difficult it is to predict weather beyond a time span longer than 4 to 10 days.

Three Scientific Methods of Weather Forecasting

Meteorologists have at their disposal three methods of predicting weather.

The analog method

It is necessary to look for former records of a situation that is identical to the present one and to find out how it evolved during subsequent days. Since such records exist now for the past century, and since computers can rapidly do this kind of search, this method appears rather promising.

The numerical method

This is the most time consuming and also the most theoretical method. The data obtained by the various weather stations are analyzed by mathematical methods based on the laws of physics. The American Von Neuman began this method in 1950 using the very first computer, called ENIAC. Today, computers of the Cray series, the world's highest-speed computers, are used in attempts to forecast weather ten days in advance.

The synoptic method

This is the simplest and fastest method. The present weather situation is examined on coded weather charts from which the evolution of the weather is predicted for the next days.

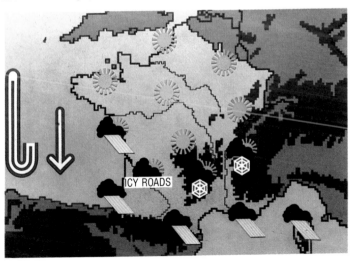

Weather forecasts displayed on television (below) or broadcast through the radio are usually quite reliable.

Weather Freaks

During the entire week we kept thinking about our planned weekend at the beach. In fact, three days ahead of time, everything necessary for the beach was ready to be packed in the trunk of the car. However, the morning before our departure, heavy rains begin. And the forecast does not inspire optimism: it predicts high winds and falling temperatures on the coast. It must be very overcast with gray skies at the beach. This is how bad weather can spoil plans for what was to be a pleasant weekend.

By the way, we could have guessed as much if we had listened to our neighbor, who for the last three days had already predicted a change in weather. She has no barometer nor any particular knowledge of meteorology: she simply suffers from arthritis. However, she assures us that when her joints hurt more than usual, the weather is going to change. She was right.

For over an hour now, he paced up and down the airport lobby. The passenger he was expecting should already have arrived in Boston. The TV monitor merely displayed "flight delayed" without any other information. Suddenly, the loudspeaker announced that the flight to Boston had been rerouted to New York because of snow. The Big Apple had better weather conditions than Boston for secure landing.

This year's crop promised to be good. As far as the eye could see, wheat rippled under a gentle breeze. Then suddenly the sky turned black. A few minutes later, the first lightning criss-crossed the sky and a severe hailstorm pounded the fields. Small ice pellets

Like all great outdoor sports, sailing depends heavily upon weather conditions. However, boats — here a Speed 770 — are increasingly better adapted to the vagaries of the sea.

crackled on the ground like bullets fired by millions of invisible celestial sharp-shooters. Less than an hour later, the crop was destroyed. The stems of the plants were lying shredded on the soil and were not to grow again.

These little anecdotes, commonplace because frequent, remind us to what extent the unpredictable antics of weather can affect not only our leisure time but also our health, transportation, or agriculture. Moreover, we are powerless against the wrath of weather.

Weather and Well-being

We all know to what extent weather acts upon our mental well-being. When the sun is shining, we tend to be happy and even-tempered, unless we have some really big worries. When it rains, we may feel depressed or irritable. It even appears that school children are more unruly in wet weather than in dry weather! At any rate, it has been demonstrated that a person can think better in dry weather and that physical efforts are more difficult when it is hot and humid than when it is cold and dry. Nevertheless, air should not be too dry because it dries our mucous membranes, as happens often in overheated rooms in winter.

It has been scientifically established that the optimal climate for the comfort of human beings corresponds to a temperature of 18°C (65°F), a humidity of 50% and almost no wind.

Fog as a Killer

Weather influences our health. For instance, bronchitis is very widespread in cold and humid counties.

In Great Britain for example, where fog is frequent, it was noticed that more deaths occurred among the elderly when fog persisted for several days. In large industrial cities, toxic vapors such as hydrogen sulfide emitted by factory stacks and exhaust pipes of cars mix with droplets of air moisture to form "smog," a contraction of smoke and fog. In 1952, smog lasted for five days in London and killed 4000 people! There-

Harsh winters at the beginning of this century. In the poor neighborhoods of some cities, people often had only public braziers to warm themselves.

after, strict regulations were enforced against air pollution, and since 1956, London has become a clean air city.

Smog exists also in Los Angeles, Santiago, and Athens. These cities are located in basins surrounded by hills that stop winds and keep polluted air in the basins.

The Crazy Wind

As mentioned earlier, a sudden lowering of pressure with the approach of a low-pressure system may cause aching joints in persons suffering from arthritis. Such persons can often thus forecast bad weather.

It has been observed that winds have marked effects on some nervous individuals, who become irritable, even aggressive. For instance, the dry, cold northerly *mistral* in France that blows down the Rhône Valley at great speed is called by the inhabitants "le vent fou" (the crazy wind). Indeed, when it becomes very strong, pressure usu-

ally falls in the lee of the Alps and a depression forms in the Gulf of Genoa. The mistral may blow for days on end and bring hardship to some people.

The *foehn* is a dry warm wind that blows down from the Alps toward Swiss and Austrian valleys. Some persons are prone to discomfort or dizziness during spells of foehn. This effect is apparently caused by accompanying infrasounds, which are sound waves with a frequency below the range of the human ear.

In Israel the *charav* blows, a wind that may cause migraine and nausea and even affect concentration. Such effects will often appear half a day before the first wind squall. Studies on the chemistry of air have shown that air has twice as many positive ions, which means that there is more electricity in the air.

In various regions, some winds are considered evil and said to be the cause of accidents, depressions, and sometimes even crimes.

Thunderstorms are also felt in advance by certain

The God of the Winds *represented by the Japanese painter Nonomura Sotatsu (17th century). According to Greek mythology, Aeolus was the ruler of the winds. This is why the word aeolian, or eolian, refers to the wind. For instance, eolian erosion describes the abrasion of rock or soil by wind.*

individuals who become nervous even before the first lightning appears. This is also due to increased atmospheric electricity.

Climates for Centenarians

We should never forget that we bathe permanently in an ocean of air. Any change in the quality of this air (temperature, humidity, ionization, particles in suspension, wind speed, and so forth) can therefore influence our mental and physical health.

There are about a dozen different major climate types on Earth and within each are found local climates that differ from the surrounding ones: these are called microclimates. Such is the case in the Isle of Wight, off the south coast of England, where blue skies and mild temperatures can be enjoyed in the middle of the rather cool and rainy English Channel. Such is the case also on the Vendée coast and the region of Font-Romeau in France or the County of Kerry at the southwestern tip of Ireland, where rhododendrons grow under the influence of the Gulf Steam, a warm ocean current coming from Florida.

However, there is no easy explanation for the beneficial influence of certain local climates on longevity and health. For instance in Hunza, in Kashmir (northern India), the percentage of centenarians (persons 100 years or older) is greater than elsewhere. Similarly, many very old people are found in the Caucasus and in parts of the Colombian Andes.

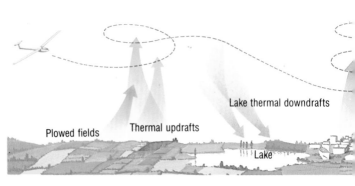

Lake thermal downdrafts

Thermal updrafts

Plowed fields

Lake

The science that studies the relationship between health and climate is called biometeorology. Its pioneer is Frederick Sargent, a professor at the University of Texas, who died in 1980. He showed that, during the winter months, our body activities are slowed down because blood capillaries that feed the cells of the skin are constricted. We thus become less resistant to contagious diseases; an increased number of heart failures is also noticed. In general, the most trying season for our health is spring, and to a lesser degree, fall. These intermediate seasons bring many changes that affect our bodies.

The Dependency of Sports upon Weather

Has it ever happened that you had to cancel an outdoor tennis game or a horseback ride in the woods because of rain? Or that you could not go windsurfing with your favorite board because there was not enough wind?

More examples could easily be found to show what an important role the weather plays in outdoor sports. Indeed, weather has a strong effect upon our leisure activities in general. Sometimes, important football games have to be interrupted or even cancelled because of pouring rain or

To fly a glider requires good meteorological knowledge. The pilot must be able to recognize thermals that will allow him to reach higher altitudes from where he can glide down.

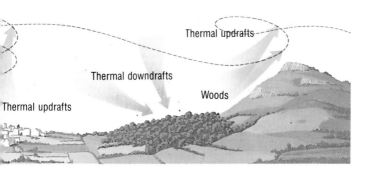

Thermal updrafts

Thermal downdrafts

Woods

Thermal updrafts

dense fog. Car rallies and races (such as the Indy 500 at Indianapolis) have to be cancelled from time to time for the same reason. People who are fond of winter sports and who spend a week or so in the Alps or the Rockies, for instance, may return home disappointed because there was not enough snow. Yachtsmen have to reschedule their sailing trips for another time when strong seas are announced. Finally, for those who fly gliders, meteorology plays an even more important role, because gliders need rather strong thermal updrafts in order to perform properly.

In Dense Fog ("Pea Soup")

In April 1912, the British liner *Titanic* was on her maiden voyage between Great Britain and the United States. With a length of 882 feet 9 inches (six times the size of the Statue of Liberty), she was the largest ship of her time and was considered "unsinkable." However, on the night of April 14, when she

Fans of ultralights *(above) wait for fair weather in order to take a safe tour in the sky.*

One of the competitors in the Paris-Dakar car race passes by *(on the left). Weather conditions are often extremely harsh. Sandstorms, in particular, in this part of the world are one of the "predicted" obstacles that men and equipment have to contend with. These storms are, in other words, part of the game.*

39

was south of Newfoundland, a gigantic iceberg suddenly materialized from the fog. The pilot on duty was unable to avoid it. Ripped open, the huge ship sank slowly into the icy waters. About 700 persons were saved in lifeboats, but more than 1500 perished.

The sinking of the *Titanic* is the greatest disaster in maritime history caused by fog, commonly called "pea soup." Fog is in fact nothing else but a cloud of moisture formed at the level of the ground, at zero altitude. The only difference between fog and clouds at high altitude is the distinct shape of the latter whereas fog has none. It is simply a blanket with a uniform upper surface as can be seen from a mountain when fog lingers at the bottom of a valley. The formation of fog also requires a complete absence of breeze.

Dangerous on Earth and in the Air

Fog is extremely dangerous for road traffic. Indeed, many crashes on highways occur in dense patches of fog that reduce visibility to below 40 meters (131 feet). It is necessary to drive very slowly. If fog spreads over a whole region, traffic becomes congested or paralyzed. Driving at night in fog is even more hazardous, because the fine water droplets in fog (1/100 millimeter in diameter) diffuse light the way smoke does. Special foglights with light beams near the road give somewhat better visibility than ordinary headlights; however, extreme care must still be taken.

At sea, when visibility is diminished but nevertheless greater than 1 kilometer (0.62 miles), moisture in the air is called haze.

Air traffic can also be crippled by fog, which can prevent planes from taking off or landing. Only large airports and the most modern jets are equipped with an Instrument Landing System, which allows them to land when visibility is virtually nil. Otherwise, airplanes have to be rerouted to another airport with clearer skies. Several methods of fog clearing exist by heating the air, generally by means of static jet engines located along runways. However, this system is expensive and only a few airports are equipped with it.

The captain of the "Titanic" had been given orders to take the shortest northern route, without paying any attention to meteorology. On the night of April 14, 1912, the ship collided with an iceberg, resulting in more than 1500 deaths.

Hazardous Skidding

Another great enemy on the road is ice. It may be formed in two ways: either when overmelted water (liquid water droplets at temperatures below the freezing point) touches the ground, or when rain falls on a frozen surface. In both cases, a thin layer of ice is formed. Roads and highways, streets and sidewalks, all become true ice sheets, hazardous for vehicles as well as for pedestrians.

Ice may also form on power or telephone lines, which then become enclosed in ice casings that increase in size during freezing rain. When the weight of the ice becomes too great, lines break and houses are without electricity and telephones. Ice also causes great problems for ships at very high latitudes—in particular for fishing trawlers. Their large superstructures may become covered with ice, making a ship so heavy that it sometimes sinks or turns over on its side. Airplanes become covered with ice when they cross clouds consisting of overmelted water droplets. This ice may weigh down the aircraft and block the control surfaces, as with the case in 1982, when an Air Florida jet fell into the Potomac River after takeoff from Washington National airport.

Snow can also cause great problems. In February 1983, when almost two feet of snow fell in the heavily populated northeastern United States, more than 3000 flights had to be cancelled during the weekend. On roads and highways, snowstorms often cause serious disruptions in traffic. In the winter of 1970-1971, thousands of cars were blocked on the French freeway to the South during the New Year's Eve holidays. Many people had to be rescued by helicopter.

Weather and Agriculture

Agriculture is certainly one of the human activities that depends most heavily upon weather conditions.

Three important features govern the climate:

—insolation—that is, the number of hours of sunshine per year, which depends not only upon cloudiness of the sky but also upon latitude, which controls the length of a day.

The Soviet icebreaker "Arctika." Operated by nuclear power, it is one of the most powerful ships of its kind.

Tree rings are an indication of a tree's age; their width also reflects former weather conditions. Rings become wider with warmer and more humid seasons.

—rainfall—that is, the number of rainy days per year and the quantity of water that falls from season to season.

—average temperature of the air, including whether or not severe frosts occur in winter.

Insolation, for instance, is important for vineyards; rainfall, for rice paddies; and the absence of frost, for the cultivation of coffee, cotton, and citrus fruit.

Changes in climate from year to year at a given location can indirectly influence cultivation by enhancing proliferation of insect pests such as aphids, grasshoppers or beetles.

Housing and Life-style

Weather not only affects our mental and physical health, but also influences very strongly our life-style, our clothes, our food, and the architecture of our houses.

It is well-known that in warm climates people spend much of their day

outdoors. Also in European countries such as Spain, Portugal, Italy, and Greece, the afternoon siesta during the hot summer months remains a tradition and it is only at night that life starts again. Anybody who has visited Spain knows that dinner is not served until about 10 p.m. and that city life goes on until the middle of the night. In contrast, the inhabitants of northern countries (Great Britain, the Netherlands, Scandinavia) leave their houses and stay outdoors less frequently.

Frequent spells of bad weather and lower temperatures force people to shun outdoor life. In France, a country located right between the two kinds of climates, the inhabitants of the northern region have a differ-

Growing zucchini in the middle of the desert. *Settlers of the Negev Desert in Israel succeeded in doing this despite the harsh climate of that region.*

ent life-style from that of people in the Mediterranean region. In the United States, however, factories, offices, universities, hospitals, public places, vehicles, and many homes are air-conditioned in summer and thoroughly heated in winter, so that work and inside leisure are no longer influenced by weather conditions.

Igloos and Huts

Inhabitants of polar regions, such as the Inuit of Alaska, Canada, and Greenland, take shelter in igloos: shallow holes that are dug in the frozen ground and covered by dome shaped structure made of blocks of hard snow. Indeed, these people have no other building material at their disposal. Nevertheless, these shelters are relatively comfortable, because the cold air can be endured more easily when it is dry and without wind. The ground surface in these igloos is covered with animal skins and furs, which provide a certain "heat" and are furthermore good protections against

The igloo is a perfect adaptation to a very harsh climate. Blocks of hard frozen snow are assembled with fresh snow, which upon freezing helps to seal the blocks together.

wind and snowstorms. The inhabitants of these inclement countries also take in calories with food rich in fat.

In tropical countries, such as Africa, it is not necessary to protect oneself against bad weather. Indeed, one can remain half-naked in the rain without catching cold, and since temperatures rarely fall below 10°C (50°F), houses do not need to be well insulated. Simple huts built with tree branches or bamboo and covered with a waterproof thatch roof or sometimes earth provide ideal houses that are well ventilated and adapted to the climate. In northern Africa, houses are built with thick walls of whitewashed stone. Openings are small, so that these houses have neither true doors nor windows. In this way, people protect themselves against high temperatures during the day and maintain, at the same time, adequate ventilation.

In temperate latitudes, houses are closed because of great temperature variations between winter and summer. Heating is necessary for several months of the year, and walls and roofs must therefore be well insulated with special materials. In northern countries, double windows (storm

Heavy clothes as protection against heat. *These young Berber girls are taking advantage of the insulating properties of wool which rejects external heat in summer and maintains body heat in winter.*

windows) or thermopanes are indispensable.

Some climatic conditions require special construction features, namely, very steep roofs in mountains or regions where snowfall is abundant (because a thick layer of snow is very heavy), or houses built on stilts in regions that are flooded during the rainy season (Thailand or Malaysia, for instance).

What Kind of Clothes Do You Wear?

Climate influences what we wear: some black people of Africa or Amerindians of the equatorial forests live almost naked because atmospheric temperature and humidity are high, whereas the inhabitants of northern regions such as Siberia clothe themselves with furs in the exceedingly cold winter months. In dry tropical regions, people cover themselves completely for protection against the sun and sandstorms. Finally, in middle latitudes, like the United States, several kinds of clothes are worn, depending on the season and on daily variation in weather. Such is not the case in polar, tropical, or equatorial regions.

Feast or Famine

Climatic conditions are of course not sufficient to determine what kinds of crops will grow in a given region, because the soil plays an important role. The extraordinary selection of French wines, for instance, is made possible because of both the nature of the soil and the difference in sunshine from one region to the other. Similarly, wheat in the United States grows best in the "wheat belt"; in France, it grows best in Beauce and Brie (in the Paris Basin). Oranges and avocados grow well in Israel, where average temperatures are much higher than in, for example, Belgium or Great Britain.

Agricultural yield is generally highest in temperate regions, which have a good balance of rain and sunshine. Tropical regions often yield only a few particular products such as lemons, dates, or peanuts. Such a low diversity of agricultural products makes these regions particularly vulnerable to a meteorological accident. Whenever catastrophic floods in Bangladesh destroy the rice crops, people suffer from extreme hunger and starvation because there is nothing else growing in that region. The same situation applies to people in Africa when droughts persist.

And sometimes weather conditions influence politics....

Meteorology on Battlefields

In the eleventh century, the Duke of Normandy, better

known as William the Conqueror, decided to invade England. However, favorable weather was needed for this enterprise to succeed. After many days of bad weather, the troops lost patience and started to disperse. Religious processions with prayers were organized along the coast … and the next day, the weather turned fair!

Nine centuries later, in that same location, an accurate scientific weather forecast enabled the Allied forces to invade Normandy on June 6, 1944, at dawn. First, rather gloomy weather was needed to let the enemy believe that nothing would happen that day; however, gradually improving weather was also necessary for an impressive quantity of war equipment to be unloaded without too many difficulties.

General George Washington also took advantage of weather conditions. The darkest chapter in his military leadership was the

Famine is common in many countries of the Third World. *It is often due to weather conditions and made worse by political conflicts, as here in Bangladesh.*

49

winter of 1776, when his disintegrating Continental Army was compelled to retreat to Pennsylvania across the Delaware River. The British had winter camps in New Jersey at Trenton and Princeton, among other cities. After Washington's surprise attack on Trenton on Christmas day, when he crossed the Delaware and captured about 900 German mercenaries, the British general Cornwallis hurried to meet the Americans. The British troops had a few skirmishes with the Continentals but then decided to wait until the next day. During the night, the wind shifted and the roads froze and Washington was able to steal away from his camp, march around Cornwallis' rear, and attack the British regiments at Princeton early on the following day.

In 1588, a change in weather favored the British fleet when it was attacked by the Spanish Armada. After several encounters, with neither side winning, the

wind suddenly shifted from northwest to southwest, forcing the Armada into open water. The English fleet followed at first but then returned home. The Armada, however, had to navigate along a dangerous route where they lost masts, sails, and food, and many of their ships were wrecked on the Irish coast. Fifty-one ships did not reach home and many thousands of Spaniards died, whereas the English lost no ship and less than 100 men in battle.

The severe conditions of the Russian winter were probably more to blame for the retreat from Moscow of Napoleon I and his army than were the attacks by Cossack cavalry. Napoleon I had underestimated the power of nature.

Napoleon I wanted to crush Russia. *He was instead defeated by the Russian winter and had to retreat. The climate was the stronger of the two.*

Meteorology of Explorers

Those who venture around the world must also take weather conditions into account. Unfavorable weather may endanger their expedition or simply have them bypass an interesting discovery. For instance, in 1579, the

English navigator Sir Francis Drake sailed past the magnificent San Francisco Bay but did not see it in the fog.

Mountaineers who climb high peaks, as in the Himalaya, must check beforehand that meteorological conditions will remain more or less favorable during their expedition. Certain times of year are better than others for this kind of undertaking. The American balloonists, Abruzzo, Anderson, and Newman, who crossed the Atlantic in "Double Eagle II" in August 1978, had to wait for adequate weather conditions. Charles Lindbergh, when he did the same crossing by airplane, had to wait until high altitude winds blew in the right direction.

Any launching of space rockets depends very much upon meteorological conditions. If the cloud cover is too low, or if winds are too strong, launchings are rescheduled. Even the most sophisticated human invention is at the mercy and the goodwill of weather.

To brave the polar seas at the time of sailboats was an extremely dangerous enterprise. The arctic summer is in fact quite short. Beginning in September or soon after, boats ran the risk of being surrounded by ice floes and crushed. If that happened, members of the crew had to debark on an ice floe in the often vain hope that it would carry them to the open sea.

When the Weather Becomes Really Bad

Winds and rainfall, hot and cold weather, all bring their share of meteorological catastrophes every year against which human beings are powerless. All we can do is to forecast the floods and the hurricanes, which sometimes allows us to restrict damage to material and to human lives. However, nature is stronger than we are and weather disasters are often considered acts of God.

Whether ocean-going fishermen or navigators, mariners have always been dependent upon the vagaries of weather and yet were also expert in the art of forecasting them.

Up to 38 miles per hour, winds are hardly dangerous. With stronger winds, things deteriorate. Between 39 and 46 miles per hour, a wind called "fresh gale" by mariners breaks off twigs of trees; between 47 and 54 miles per hour, a "strong gale" causes structural damage (chimneys or shingles torn off); between 55 and 63 miles per hour, a "whole gale" uproots trees; and finally, above 75 miles per hour, we are talking about a hurricane.

A storm can turn a simple boat ride into a tragedy. It happens indeed that a small low-pressure system may form rapidly and locally before weather stations can forecast it. This is shown by a rather sudden drop in barometric pressure. With a barometer, we can thus ourselves predict the coming of a storm without having to rely upon official weather forecasts. In Brittany (France), six killer storms were recorded in the last twenty years. The Mediterranean Sea cannot be trusted either, because sudden storms can be very violent and take many sailing fans by surprise. In the United States, the most violent kind of storm is the tornado, discussed in a later section of this book. An extreme low-pressure system arrives suddenly and can be easily noticed on household barometers.

Tropical Cyclones

The typhoon of the Pacific Ocean and the hurricane of the Atlantic are both tropical cyclones, gigantic vortexes about 300 to 900 kilometers (180 to 560 miles) in diameter. Winds reach their highest velocity between 160 to 320 kilometers per hour (100 to 200 miles per hour), in the vicinity of the eye, whereas the eye itself is an area of near calm measuring about 24 to 32 kilometers (15 to 20 miles) across. The cyclone moves rather slowly: only about 30 kilometers per hour (18 miles per hour). Hurricanes are formed in early fall over ocean waters heated to more than 26°C (80°F). A column of hot air begins to whirl around it-

Tlaloc is very famous in Mexico. He is the Aztec god of rain. The Aztec culture inherited him from the Toltec civilization that flourished in the ninth century A.D. For these people of tropical regions, rain was of the greatest importance: Tlaloc was in fact one of their main gods.

self, then becomes larger and finally drifts westward, in the opposite direction of the Earth's rotation. Moisture is condensed into enormous clouds, which soon cause torrential rains. However, instead of erupting itself, a hurricane keeps absorbing moist hot air over the ocean and continues its course. Only when passing inland, will it lose much of its force by the effects of friction.

Most hurricanes start at about 5° latitude (never at the equator) and move to-

Satellite image of a hurricane. *The colors correspond to variations of temperature inside the hurricane. It is thus possible to forecast in what direction the storm will develop.*

This aircraft is flying in the eye of a hurricane *measuring its path and speed of movement. For pilots of the United States Weather Bureau, this is an ordinary job.*

Above right *is shown the dangerous zone of a hurricane.*

ward the 30th latitude north. Those that affect the West Indies and the Gulf of Mexico may originate off Dakar (Senegal). The name "hurricane," used in North America, was derived from "Huracan," a god of storms in the West Indies, called

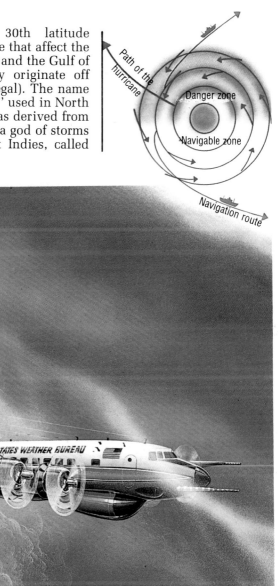

Path of the hurricane

Danger zone

Navigable zone

Navigation route

Names of Hurricanes

For a quarter of a century, meteorologists have given women's names to hurricanes. Some of them have remained notoriously famous. For instance, Hyacinthe (1980) caused torrential rains on the island of Réunion (about 19 feet in one week). Agnes (1972) caused 118 deaths in Maryland; Shirley and Ruth (1971), 55 deaths between them in Japan; Anita and Celia (1970), 20 and 14 deaths respectively in Japan and in Florida; Camille (1969), 256 deaths in Louisiana; and Betsy (1965), 75 deaths in Florida. The most destructive in the last 15 years were Joan, with 600 victims in the Philippines in 1970, and Fifi, with more than 8000 missing people in the Philippines in 1974. The deadliest and costliest hurricane in the United States occurred at Galveston (Texas) in 1900, causing 6000 deaths.

Masculine names have also been given to hurricanes in the past few years. For instance, Allen (1980) caused 272 deaths in Texas; David was responsible for thousands of casualties in the West Indies; and Frederick caused damage in Florida and Alabama in 1979.

"ouragan" in the French-speaking islands of the West Indies. In Australia, tropical cyclones are named willy-willies; in the Philippines, baguios; and in Southeast Asia, typhoons. Florida and Texas have an average of two hurricanes per year, and one every three years may cause severe damage.

Can Hurricane Damage Be Reduced?

It is known that hurricanes cause torrential rains that correspond to about one quart of water per minute in a container 39 inches in diameter! These storms occur most often along the east coast of the United States, and in Japan, Australia, the

Philippines, Madagascar, Mozambique, India, the West Indies, and parts of Mexico, but rarely in Europe, South America and Africa. The energy output of a hurricane during its entire course is ten times higher than that of a small atomic bomb!

Tropical cyclones become particularly hazardous to human beings when they cause extremely high waves upon reaching a coastal area. In 1970, such waves invaded inland areas in Pakistan and destroyed everything in their path, killing a million people.

Hurricanes that hit the coast of the United States anywhere between Texas and Maine, can cause severe damage to poorly built cottages, motels, and beachfront hotels, and even to high-rise condominiums. Studies show that in the past developers have leveled existing sand dunes and built motels less than 30 feet from the water. When hurricane Eloise struck in September 1975, it destroyed seawalls and undermined buildings, some of which collapsed. Even a 14-story building, built on pilings, would have been in danger of collapsing had the storm moved more slowly, pounding against the pilings

for a longer period of time. Indeed, concrete had been stripped from many pilings and metal rods were exposed. It is obvious that houses built along these coastal areas are at the mercy of potential hurricane disasters.

The Dangerous Funnels of Tornadoes

Among the disasters caused by high winds are tornadoes, which are vortexes of rapidly moving air. The average speed of a tornado in the midwestern part of the United States is 65 kilometers per hour (40 miles per hour), but some move as fast as 110 kilometers per hour (68.7 miles per hour). Within the funnel, winds may reach much higher speeds, up to 600 kilometers per hour (375 miles per hour). A tornado is a column of air, not wider than 2 kilometers (1.25 miles) in diameter, sometimes accompanied by extremely severe thunderstorms. The funnel shape seems to hang down from a cloud and to touch the ground for some time and then to rise again. Where it touches down, great destruction occurs in a few seconds over a limited path, which is usually not wider than 0.5 kilometers (545

What Not to Do During a Thunderstorm

Thunderstorms are extremely dangerous meteorological phenomena. Lightning strikes thousands of times per year in the United States as well as in other countries. France alone has recorded a hundred deaths per year. Thunderstorms are caused by large clouds with vertical structure, such as cumulonimbus. Electrical charges inside these clouds are reversed with respect to the ground, and from time to time luminous discharges shoot out in the form of lightning. Compressed air produced by this discharge gives a muffled sound resembling the rolling of drums: this is thunder.

Lightning, the electrical discharge from the cloud, usually hits tall metallic objects. That is why buildings are protected by metallic lightning rods that attract lightning and lead it to the ground so that the building itself is not damaged.

During thunderstorms, do not:

—take shelter under a lone tree (in particular, an oak tree or a poplar, which are the two most often hit trees because they are tall);

—stay in an air draft;

—take a bath or a shower;

—protect yourself underneath an umbrella with metallic ribs;

—remain alone in an open field;

—fix your TV antenna.

On the other hand, if you are inside your car, stay there. The steel frame provides insulation from the ground and forms what physicists call a Faraday shield. Lightning cannot penetrate inside.

yards) and rarely more than 25 kilometers (15.6 miles) long. The most destructive force is a 160 to 320 kilometers per hour (100 to 200 miles per hour) updraft at the center of the funnel that can suck up houses, cattle, and cars into the air and carry them hundreds of feet. Most of the damage done is the result not only of wind, but of a very rapid drop of atmospheric pressure that may cause outward collapse of the roof and walls of build-

ings. An average of 124 tornadoes hit the United States each year. They form when an active cold front moves into moist, unstable air. Several questions remain unanswered about how a tornado begins.

Disasters Caused by Water

Besides all the disasters caused by high waves during the hurricane season, earthquakes, or by volcanic erup-

When the air becomes charged with electricity (often after a hot summer day), lightning crosses the sky from one cloud to the other or between clouds and the ground. An imminent thunderstorm is indicated by a sky that looks similar to this.

tions, devastating floods also occur, particularly in spring. Water from torrential thundershowers, in addition to water from melting snow and ice, may cause rivers and streams to abandon their riverbed and flood the surrounding fields and roads, thus interrupting traffic and transforming city streets into canals. Farms are cut off from the rest of the world and inhabitants must sometimes be rescued by helicopter while livestock drowns.

The ancient Egyptians had to face the flooding of the Nile, and the Chinese at the time of Imperial China, the flooding of the Yellow River and the Yang Tse Kiang. These were the first people

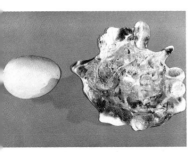

Blossoming fruit trees *are very sensitive to hail. There is no effective way to avoid hail showers except by stringing special nets above orchards.*

On the left: *The size of an exceptionally large hailstone compared with that of an egg.*

This satellite picture shows the morphology of a desert soil chiseled by the wind. It is the Grand Erg Oriental between Algeria and Libya.

who attempted to control floods, building long dikes of stone along the river where the plain was at its lowest level. Not much else can be done. Nevertheless, the Chinese continued to suffer cata- strophic floods. Three times in one century (1887, 1931, and 1969) such floods oc- curred, each claiming a mil- lion casualties.

In some regions of South- east Asia and in the Bay of

Bengal, the population suffers great hardship during the monsoon rains. These are beneficial for crops in the northern section but cause disastrous floods in the coastal areas in May and October of every year. In November 1970, 400,000 persons perished in a monsoon in Eastern Pakistan.

Damage Caused by Droughts

It seems paradoxical that some people perish because of too much water whereas others starve to death because of droughts. The situation in the Sahel is well-known: half a dozen countries between the latitudes of 15° and 20°, extending from the Atlantic Ocean to the Red Sea, suffer cruelly from a drought that started in 1968. Vegetation has disappeared everywhere, herds have become sparse, and the desert is advancing. In Mauritania, Mali, Chad, and Ethiopia, countries which suffered through

Reforestation is absolutely necessary to reestablish a climatic equilibrium in regions undergoing deforestation. However, many years are needed for a tree to grow.

an earlier drought in 1973, famine has again reached alarming proportions. Droughts also exist in countries of the southern African tropics, from Angola to Mozambique. A total of 36 African countries out of 50, or three out of four, are hit by this climatic disaster, which one finds also in South America, in Brazilian Noreste.

Some climatologists explain this phenomenon by the presence of anticyclones, which persist for a long time within the tropics and which during the rainy season displace toward the equator or the temperate regions the disturbances that might bring water. At Gao, in Mali (West Africa), only 6 centimeters (2.4 inches) of water fell in 1984, against 30 centimeters (12 inches) in normal years. With droughts appear diseases: cholera for human beings and cattle plague for the rare animals that have survived famine.

Look Out for Avalanches!

Everybody knows that there must be sufficient snow for skiing; thus the date of the first snow is of great importance for the opening of winter sports resorts. However, the snow must not only be abundant, but it must also have a certain quality, because some snow conditions are totally unfit for downhill skiing. The study of snow has become a science.

For skiers, in particular those practicing cross-country skiing, the main danger is avalanches. Warming trends in spring or a layer of ice formed underneath a certain thickness of fresh snow can cause an avalanche. A small amount of snow starts to slip and becomes larger the farther it goes down the slope, incorporating snow, then earth and pebbles in its path. Those who have made a snowman know the snowball effect. An avalanche descending a mountain slope carries everything along with it; when it has reached a certain size and a certain speed, nothing can stop it. Barriers against avalanches (wooden stakes driven in the ground) are only effective in the early stages of sliding. Every year, numerous skiers are carried away by avalanches, too often the victims of their own recklessness in spite of security measures and repeated warnings. We now have maps indicating danger zones, because avalanches occur almost always at the same places. Nevertheless, some skiers continue to venture beyond marked trails.

Avalanches are common in the Alps (France, Switzerland, Italy, Austria) and kill hundreds of local inhabitants. The most devastating of all hit the village of Blons (Vorarlberg, Austria) on January 11, 1954, when two avalanches wiped out 29 houses in a village of 90, killing 115 people.

At Sea and in the Air

Sailboat enthusiasts who take part in the famous transatlantic races know to what extent good weather forecasts are important in order for them to win. Depending upon the location and the movement of high- and low-pressure systems on the ocean, several sailing routes are possible between Europe and the United States.

In order to choose the best route, navigators should look carefully at weather maps before sailing. It may be advantageous to select a longer route along which favorable winds will let you gain a few valuable hours.

In a similar way, air currents exist at high altitudes that may cut the flight between Paris and New York, sometimes by more than half an hour. Before each takeoff for any one destination, captain and copilot prepare their flight itinerary with great care in order to choose the best air route with respect to weather conditions. They want to avoid zones of strong turbulence (for the comfort and security of passengers), and also to look for the most favorable winds for a minimum use of fuel. It was the development of commercial aviation in the fifties that gave a boost to the establishment of weather forecasting. For air traffic, forecasts are made every three hours. What will tomorrow bring?

When much snow has fallen in the mountains, the risk of avalanches makes cross-country skiing outside marked trails hazardous.

Meteorology Yesterday and Tomorrow

People often complain that the weather is not what it used to be—because of an unusually mild spell in November or a late frost in May. They conclude that these changes are caused by supersonic jets, nuclear explosions, or artificial satellites.

In the eighteenth century, Bernardin de Saint-Pierre (author who was known for his love of nature and disdain of society), accused the compass of changing the weather with its magnetic needle! The first railways with steam locomotives were also accused of all the weather calamities occurring at the time. Let us not forget that the most powerful man-made objects release only an insignificant amount of energy compared to that released by atmospheric phenomena such as storms, tornadoes, or hurricanes. Even though the explosion of an atomic bomb causes heavy damage locally (we are not talking here about long-range effects on living beings), at the scale of the whole planet, the energy released by an atomic bomb is a mere trifle. More important, however, are inconspicuous processes, such as the release into the atmosphere of carbon dioxide resulting from the combustion of coal, natural gas, and oil.

About 6000 years ago, in the heart of the Tassili plateau (Sahara), grass savanna fed herds of cattle. Today, this region is an uninhabitable desert.

It is important to understand that we are short-sighted so far as the weather goes. The climate of our planet has in fact cyclic variations of either several thousand or several million years. The variations in climate that we can perceive in a few years, or even during an entire lifetime, are only minor episodes in a grand scheme.

A recently developed field of science, called paleoclimatology, is trying to reconstruct the climate of former centuries and millennia on the basis of written text (letters, church archives, newspapers); the study of tree rings, the analysis of the composition of ice in deep cores in Antarctica, and the identification of pollen grains buried in old layers of peat. At present, we do know that the past climate was a succession of glaciations of long duration, interrupted

A moment in the life of prehistoric hunters in their shelters when Europe underwent a glacial period. Lamps burned animal fat.

For some hundreds of thousands of years, snow has accumulated on the Antarctic continent. It resembles a huge layercake with trapped air bubbles, volcanic ash, and micrometeorites. When drilling cores in this ice, scientists can uncover a great amount of information about the former climates on our planet.

by shorter interglacial periods. The last glaciation ended about 10,000 years ago and we are thus on the way toward a new cold period which may begin in 5000 years. But until then, climates will show other fluctuations, some of which might even make us believe that the Earth's climate is getting warmer. Climatic cycles are caused by, among other factors, variations of the terrestrial orbit around the sun, as was suggested by the Yugoslav geophysicist Milutin Milankovitch as early as 1941.

As a result, during glacial periods, there was less water in liquid state and hence the sea level dropped. Indeed, 10,000 years ago, shorelines were about 90 meters (300 feet) lower than today. The English Channel (now between Great Britain and France) was then the lower portion of the Seine River Valley, and the Thames River was a tributary of the Rhine! In the Mediterranean Sea, Corsica and Sardinia were joined to form only one island. The Bering Strait, during a short span of time, including and following the last glacial advance, was partially dry land and allowed human beings to walk from Siberia to Alaska. Most sci-

Air Pollution

Air is easily polluted. Mixed with fog, fumes from factory stacks can pollute the air of large cities. However, natural pollution also exists. For instance, ashes spewed out during large volcanic eruptions may drift several times around the Earth, carried by jet streams in the atmosphere at an altitude of 15 or 20 kilometers (9.3 or 12.5 miles). One of the three most powerful volcanic eruptions in historical times is that of Krakatoa (a volcanic island in Indonesia) in 1883. It released such a large amount of dust that the sky in Europe had an abnormal color for two years. Some products of this eruption were even found recently in the ice of Antarctica. Many scientists believe that such layers of ashes suspended in the atmosphere can cause temporary climatic changes.

Moreover, a rather common phenomenon is transportation of large quantities of sand from the Sahara and surrounding desert regions. This sand, lifted by local storms and carried by high-altitude air currents, eventually falls to the ground in countries lying to the north, such as Spain, France, and sometimes even Great Britain, when the sand mixes with water droplets in clouds. Yellowish or sometimes red rainfalls (when laterite, an African red soil, mixes with sand) are frequently recorded. The last ones occurred in the Landes (western France) on July 12, 1982, and in Paris and northern France on November 9, 1984.

entists are convinced that Asian populations crossed over at that point and invaded the American continent without even realizing that they had gone from one continent to another. When European explorers discovered the Americas in the fifteenth and sixteenth centuries, they thus encountered American Indians that had descended from Asian stock.

Will Man Change the Climate?

In Africa, sorcerers called "rainmakers" still exist. For a long time now, people have tried to influence the weather and, in particular, to produce the rain showers so necessary for agriculture. One method consists of lighting huge fires, which cause warm air to rise and to condense into clouds; unfortunately, showers have rarely resulted.

It is possible today to induce rain from an existing cloud by seeding it, using various chemicals such as sodium chloride or silver iodide in crystals. These products are scattered from airplanes or from special

A "Little Ice Age" spread over Europe in the seventeenth century, as evidenced in this painting by Bruegel. By contrast, the climate was abnormally warm in 1930. Maybe a new warming trend will occur about 2015.

rockets slightly larger than those used in fireworks. Most often, cloud seeding is used to start a hailstorm before the threatening cumulonimbus has drifted above fragile crops. Anti-hail rockets are frequently employed by farmers and winegrowers. It is a fact that hailstorms cause great damage in winegrowing countries as well as in wheatgrowing areas. For instance, in France the damage to crops from hail amounts to 1 billion French francs per year, that is 1% of agricultural yields. People have also learned how to heat air with rows of gas flares or with reactors pointing to the sky. This technique permits planes to land in airports that are covered with a dense layer of fog.

This is about all we can do with present-day techniques. It is certainly out of the question that we may ever be able to change weather on a large scale. This is probably for the best, because fair weather for some is not necessarily fair weather for others and might be the source of new conflicts. For quite some time to come, we shall remain at the mercy of the vagaries of weather. It is up to us to be able to predict them.

Index

Numbers in italics refer to illustrations.

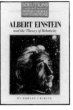